Contents

C000218024

Introduction ....

About the Romans...

Section A: The Rise and Fall of an Empire 7
    A1 The Geography of Roman Britain
    A2 The Roman Occupation of Britain
    A3 Areas and Empires
    A4 The Roman War Machine
    A5 A Day in the Life of Tony Rough

Section B: Number Words and Number Symbols 13
    B1 Everyday Numbers
    B2 A Roman Milestone
    B3 Roman Multiplication
    B4 Big Numbers
    B5 Roman Number Word-Search

Section C: Emperors, Gods, Coins and Calendars 19
    C1 Gods and Calendars
    C2 Fractions and Roman Coins
    C3 The Seven-Day Week
    C4 Games, Gods and Gambling
    C5 Hypatia of Alexandria

Section D: Measurement 25
    D1 The Measure of Man
    D2 Weighing Meat
    D3 Walls and Ditches
    D4 The *Groma*
    D5 Measuring Corn

Section E: Shape and Pattern in Roman Art 31
    E1 Mosaics
    E2 Rome in Africa
    E3 Shape, Space and Cross-Sections
    E4 Mosaic from Pompeii
    E5 The Pelta Mosaic Pattern

Resource Sheets 37
    R1   Roman Britain
    R2   Timeline of the Roman Occupation of Britain
    R3   The Roman Empire
    R4   Roman Numerals
    R5   Big Numbers
    R6   Roman Inscriptions
    R7   Roman Coins
    R8   Mosaic Grid
    R9   Mosaic Designs
    R10 *Duodecim Scripta* ('Twelve Lines')

Activity Record Sheet 47

Credits...48

Introduction

Aims

This is the third Activity Book in the series 'Mathematics from History'. Like the other two, on the Egyptians and the Greeks, it is aimed principally at 7–11 year olds, but will engage children from 5 to 13 years old.

The aims of the book are to:

- Use history as a rich resource to stimulate mathematical thinking and activity.
- Demonstrate how mathematical ideas are not only useful today, but also were essential in everyday life throughout the Roman period.
- Encourage the use of mathematics in history and of history in mathematics.

Methods

Recent Government publications have stressed the importance of 'maintaining breadth and balance'. A sound way of doing this uses 'whole world' learning as in the activities presented here. By doing them, pupils will encounter real history as well as mathematics. Literacy, oracy and teamwork skills will also be enhanced, and they will work towards a 'seamless web' of learning, rather than one dictated by official curriculum categories.

This book provides numerous opportunities for pupils to apply and consolidate skills acquired in literacy, mathematics and IT lessons in work in other subjects. In it you will find:

- **Ten Resource Sheets.** These are designed to be photocopied, and have a range of uses within and beyond the study of this book. Most of them will not be written on and are re-usable. Therefore they can usefully be copied onto card and even laminated.
- **Twenty-five Activity Sheets.** There are five main sections, each with five Activity Sheets designed to be photocopied for use by each pupil. There is space at the top for the user's name and date (which need not be written in Roman numerals!). Many of the Activity Sheets make use of specific Resource Sheets, as indicated by the thumbnail at the top left.
- **An Activity Record Sheet.** This is designed to go at the front of each pupil's Personal Portfolio, and will maintain a progress record and encourage pupils to reflect on the learning experience.
- **Teacher Notes.** Each section is introduced with a page of notes to help teachers make best use of the Activity Sheets.

Pupils may use the back of Activity Sheets where necessary, and can collect their completed sheets into a Personal Portfolio.

At the bottom of each Activity Sheet is a **Gladiator Challenge**. This will test able pupils and stretch the imagination of all. If used as an option, the Gladiator Challenge can help with class management, as it provides material for those who otherwise would finish before the rest.

Running up the side of each Activity Sheet is a **Trivium** in small print. This is just an interesting snippet of information designed to enhance and extend the Activity. Children love trivia, and you can devise your own 'Trivium Quizzium' as a fun activity if you wish. (NB: These play-uses of Latin should not be shown to your classics teacher! Trivium originally meant the three areas of knowledge first studied by scholars; after that came the four areas of the *quadrivium* which were presumably less trivial.)

Classroom Use

You should work through the Activity Sheets yourself before presenting them in class. A key aim is to weld pupils' (and teachers'!) 'mathematics brain' and 'history brain' so they support, rather than conflict with, each other.

You might sometimes stress the differences between mathematical and non-mathematical ways of thinking. Mathematics requires art as well as science and, just as in other subjects, expansive and visionary imagination is required along with systematic rigour and due regard for evidence.

The welding of mathematics and history provides many opportunities. We all see how the past and the future can prompt children's curiosity and excite their sense of wonder – from dinosaurs to space travel. Their questions and statements invariably tap into the mathematical arenas of shape, measure, number, pattern, data and evidence:

- How old is it?
- How big was it?
- How much did it weigh?
- Why is it that shape?
- How do you know that?

There are also questions of intent which require mathematics to answer them:

- How did they build it?

...and questions of methodology which focus on the scientific notion of 'reliable evidence':

- How sure can we be?

Indeed, the key questions of history are often key questions in maths and science.

- Why did something happen?
- How is it related to other happenings?
- What is the evidence?

Pure mathematics is perhaps the most stringent discipline with regard to evidence, and one might claim that it is actually impossible to teach history adequately without tapping into key mathematical ideas. The converse is also true.

A parallel and strategically important reflection is that mathematics teaching needs curriculum areas such as history in order to demonstrate its value and power – 'unreasonable efficacy', as it has been called. Also, as Tim Copeland has written: 'Maths that is taught without reference to its power to explain real problems is a stilted maths, like learning to speak without ever having a conversation.'

Teachers will develop their own structures for interpreting these relationships. But one model, based on Copeland, is the following:

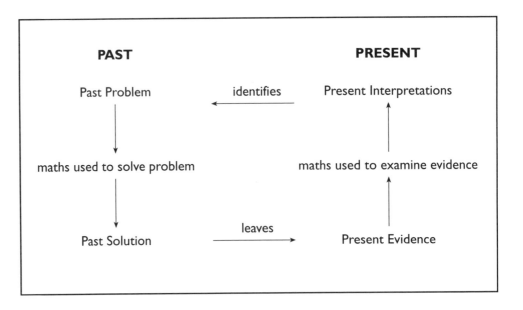

The loop can be entered at any point. Starting in the top-left corner, it suggests that:

- Past Problems (e.g. how to build a road) are interpreted using present-day interpretations.
- Past Problems were solved using mathematics, giving a 'Past Solution' (e.g. the road).
- The Past Solution becomes (or fails to become) Present Evidence.
- We also use mathematics to examine Present Evidence; this feeds into the interpretations we are able to give of the past – and so the cycle continues.

About the Romans

This book is about the Romans, for us one of the most important groups of people who ever lived. The heyday of their Empire was from about 100 BC to AD 400 – this included the time when they occupied Britain. Their influence is still here and throughout Europe today.

The Romans were important in collecting and transmitting ideas from earlier civilisations, including the Babylonians, Egyptians and Greeks. These ideas included mathematics, and the Romans were particularly strong on applications.

With the ideas they inherited and developed, the Romans were able to control a large empire of sometimes unruly people. Their lasting legacy was to bring these ideas and applications to outlying areas, including Britain.

As you study the Romans, you might like to ask yourself: 'How different would Britain be today if the Romans had not been here?' You will probably conclude: 'Very different.'

As you will see, mathematical ideas were central to many areas of Roman life, just as they are today. You cannot build roads, plan towns, engage in war or feed armies without mathematics and its concepts of data, number, symmetry, shape and size, and so on. However, generally in Roman times these ideas were developed by ordinary practical people. Unlike the Greeks, the Romans tended not to have specialist mathematicians.

Mathematics enters all areas of everyday life, even when we are not aware of it. Each one of us constructs our own world of mathematics to help us through life.

Throughout the book you will find the following logos:

This means that the pupils need to write on a separate sheet of paper (or on the back of the Activity Sheet).

This means that they will need a calculator (otherwise, calculators are generally not needed).

Introduction

The aim of this Section is to locate Roman Britain in time and space, and also to emphasise the key role of the army in enforcing Roman rule. In it, pupils will explore the following topics and skills:

A1 The Geography of Roman Britain
- use maps and scales
- estimate and describe distances and directions

A2 The Roman Occupation of Britain
- calculate times and timespans using BC and AD
- write and relate BC and AD to historical events

A3 Areas and Empires
- estimate areas using grid squares
- calculate areas

A4 The Roman War Machine
- visualise numbers in the form of rectangular blocks
- calculate figures needed by army planners

A5 A Day in the Life of Tony Rough
- relate verbal descriptions to movements on a map
- calculate distances; add distances; make and understand approximations

Extensions

This section aims to embed the learning of mathematical ideas within the development of a sound and sympathetic historiography.

A1

Introduce a map of present-day Britain; compare it with the towns and roads of Roman Britain.

Discuss the use of grid-squares on maps and their use for calculating areas (see A3), measuring distance, and identifying location using grid co-ordinates.

Emphasise the difference between 'eyeball' estimation, 'considered' estimation, and measurement and calculation. Discuss appropriate contexts for each.

A2

Discuss the words *Anno Domini*, and their links with words such as 'annual', 'dominant', 'domineering', etc. Even the word 'dominoes' has the same root – the pieces suggest white eyes peering out from a monk's black hooded habit, also called 'domino'. (The best translation of *dominus* is 'lord' or 'master'; Scottish schoolmasters are still called 'dominie'.)

Discuss 'BC', and the secular alternative 'BCE' (Before the Common Era). But note that Jesus was almost certainly not born in the year 0, or even in the year 1.

The BC/AD terminology, and the idea that Jesus was born on 25 December, only became current after Dionysius Exiguus in AD 525, by which time the truth of the matter was shrouded in mystery and mystification. Note that there was no year 0. This can complicate calculations – e.g. 100 years before AD 90 is not 10 BC but 11 BC. However, this point does not need labouring here! (Note too, that it is usual to write 'AD 100' but '100 BC'.)

The last question needs knowledge of Roman numerals (see Section B).

A3

This activity emphasises how small Britain is compared with the whole Roman Empire. Also, there was as much of the Roman Empire on the other side of Rome (east and south into Asia and Africa) as there was between Rome and Britain.

A4

The plan view of a rectangular block of soldiers is reflected in Rome's urban planning, where city blocks are also called 'centuries'.

You might like to extend the rectangular block concept, and ask questions about other possible ways of arranging the internal centuries and cohorts. How would the pupils arrange the blocks if there were different numbers of soldiers involved?

A5

In this activity, encourage pupils to visualise themselves walking around the map of York. Draw it on the playground, and let their imaginations drive the mathematics. Ask how far you really walk when going 100m through town – including all diversions, side steps and so on.

Times are given in Roman numerals – for example, IV = 4. For more work on Roman numerals see Section B.

The Geography of Roman Britain

NAME .... DATE ....

You will need Resource Sheet R1 'Roman Britain'.

Roman Britain

- Put a dot on this map to show where you live.

- Using the map and scale, check the following statement:

  'York is approximately 350km north of London.'

- **Now complete the following sentences.**

  - Lincoln is approximately .... km .... of London.
  - Chester is approximately .... km .... of London.
  - Dover is approximately .... km .... of London.
  - Where I live is approximately .... km .... of London.

- **Which town marked on the map is nearest to where you live?**

  ....

- **Complete the following sentence for the town on the map that is nearest to where you live:**

  .... is approximately .... km from where I live in a ....erly direction.

- **Now write out the above sentence on the back of this sheet, filling in the gaps, for three other towns on the map.**

- **Using the map, estimate the following lengths:**

  - Hadrian's Wall is approximately .... km long.
  - The Fosse Way is approximately .... km long.
  - Watling Street is approximately .... km long.
  - Ermine Street is approximately .... km long.

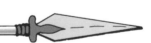

If you were a Roman soldier marching the length of Hadrian's Wall, how long would it take? How long would it take you to walk from there to London?

TRIVIUM Roman names often end in 'um' (or rather, 'vm', because the Latin alphabet had no 'u'). This includes place names like *Londinium* (London), *Eboracum* (York) and *Verulamium* (St Albans).

The Roman Occupation of Britain

NAME .... DATE ....

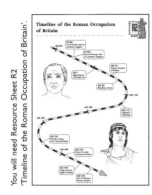

You will need Resource Sheet R2 'Timeline of the Roman Occupation of Britain'.

The Christian calendar counts its years from the birth of Jesus:

- BC stands for 'Before Christ', so 100 BC is 100 years before Christ was born.

- AD stands for 'Anno Domini' (which is Latin for 'Year of the Lord'), so AD 100 is 100 years after Christ was born.

Which came first:

- 55 BC or 54 BC? ....

- AD 55 or AD 54? ....

Using the timeline, complete the following:

- There were .... years between the Roman invasion of Britain in AD 43 and Boudicca's revolt in ....

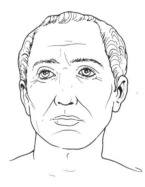

- Hadrian's Wall was built in ....
  That was .... years before the
  Romans starting leaving Britain in ....

Now, on the back of this sheet, write some sentences of your own like the ones above (with gaps), and ask your friends to complete them.

Now try some using only Roman numerals!

Gladiator CHALLENGE

How many years were there between the first Roman raid on Britain and when they started leaving? What percentage of this period was BC? What percentage was AD?

TRIVIUM We are not sure when Jesus was really born. Some evidence suggests he was born in 4 BC. There is no year 0: after 1 BC comes AD 1.

Areas and Empires

NAME .... DATE ....

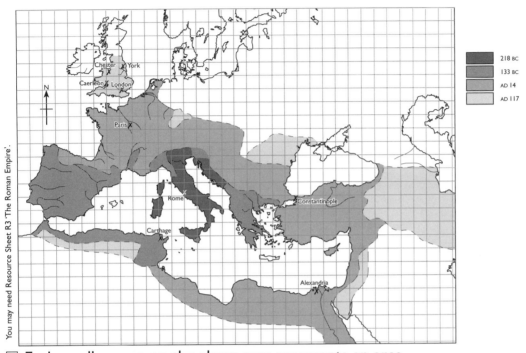

218 BC
133 BC
AD 14
AD 117

Chester X York
Caerleon X London
Paris X
Rome
Constantinople
Carthage
Alexandria

You may need Resource Sheet R3 'The Roman Empire'.

☐ Each small square on the above map represents an area approximately 200 km by 200 km.

🪙 **Estimate and then calculate how many of these squares fit into:**

	Estimate	Calculation
(a) the part of Britain that was occupied by the Romans	....	....
(b) the Roman Empire in 218 BC	....	....
(c) the Roman Empire in AD 117	....	....

📝 🪙 **On the back of this sheet, write out the number of square kilometres represented by each of your answers above.**

🪙 **How many times is (c) bigger than (b)?** .... **times**

🪙 **How many times is (c) bigger than (a)?** .... **times**

📝 🪙 **Now write some area questions of your own, and try them out on your friends.**

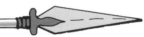

List as many as you can of today's countries that were in the Roman Empire.
Which is the largest?
Which is the smallest?

TRIVIUM The historian Polybius (c.201–c.120 BC) marvelled at how 'almost the whole inhabited world came under the sole rule of the Romans within just 53 years' (220–168 BC).

The Roman War Machine

NAME .... DATE ....

In AD 120 the Romans had three legions in Britain:

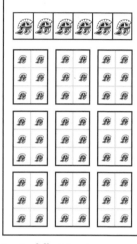

Legio II: Augusta (Caerleon)

Legio VI: Victrix (York)

Legio XX: Valeria Victrix (Chester)

- Each legion had ten cohorts. (One was bigger than the others.)

- Each cohort had six centuries, each of 80 to 100 men.

How many soldiers was this in all? .... to .... **soldiers**

Most soldiers ate 1 to 2 kg of food each day.

How much would a legion eat in a week? .... to .... **kg**

(or .... **to** .... **tonnes).**

(1 tonne = 1000 kg)

Imagine you are cooking for a cohort.
Write out your menus for a day and prepare a shopping list.

Imagine there is an uprising at Lunt, near Coventry. If you were in charge of the Roman army, how many soldiers would you send from each of the three legions? Write about what else you would do.

TRIVIUM The word 'century' usually means 100 years, but here it means a group of 80 to 100 men. (Originally centuries had 100 men, but by AD 120 most had around 80 men.)

A Day in the Life of Tony Rough

NAME .... DATE ....

Antoninus Rufinianus is a Roman soldier based at York (*Eboracum*).

Find and mark the following places on the diagram:

- the barracks (where he sleeps)
- two sets of baths
- four fortress gates
- the bridge over the river
- the arrow pointing north, and the scale representing 100 metres

Below is the story of Tony's day.

Draw on the map the route he takes.

Estimate how far he walks.

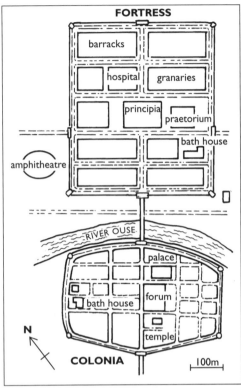

Map of Roman York about AD 300

After waking at IV of the clock, I crossed the river to visit the baths. I then had an egg for breakfast with my dear Angelina who lives outside the north-east gate of the fortress, by my barracks.

At VI of the clock I reported for work at the Principia, where the Commandant sent me on an errand to the forum. After that I walked round the fortress wall three times, making sure that everything was in order.

Then I had lunch with my century. In the afternoon, we marched up and down outside the long fortress wall, ten times in each direction.

Finally I went to the baths again, inside the fortress this time, and returned to my barracks.

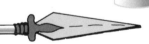

Gladiator CHALLENGE

Imagine you had a day in Roman York. Describe your day, and work out how far you walk.

TRIVIUM Constantine (AD 274–337) was declared Emperor in York in AD 306. His mother was Christian, and he converted to Christianity on his deathbed — an important event for the survival of the church, and for the decline of Rome.

Introduction

The aim of this Section is to explore the diverse ways in which the Romans used their number system. Contrary to what is often supposed and taught in schools, the Roman system of numerals was very variable according to time and place (hardly surprising given the size and duration of the Roman civilisation). It even varied according to the whim and inventiveness of individual users. This still presents problems. For example, if you try to represent 1999, anything is possible from the additive MDCCCCLXXXXVIIII to the subtractive minimalism of MIM.

The Romans had excruciating ways of writing big numbers, they had no zero and no base system – and none of this was conducive to doing arithmetic. (This was one reason for the development of the Roman counting-board or horizontal abacus – but that is another story.)

Extensions

B1

There are opportunities here for Roman clock-mathematics: 'It's X of the clock, what time will it be in III hours?' and so on.

It is important to emphasise that Roman numbering could follow several conventions. There were several ways you could write a number, say 13; some that are mathematically possible but not actually used. (For example VVIII and even IIII IIII III).

Conventions developed in different ways: clock faces usually have IIII not IV (and yet IX not VIIII). Historically, subtractive forms such as IV and IX became dominant only in the Middle Ages, but the notion that there is just one 'correct' way and that all other ways are 'wrong' is a modern, perhaps Victorian, error.

B2

There is scope here for reading 'real' Roman numerals (not always an easy task), and for celebrating the diversity and inventiveness of styles (many teachers may be surprised to learn that XXCIIII could correctly represent 84).

There is a lot of folklore about the origins of Roman numerals. For example: I to IIII represent fingers; V represents an open palm; M means mille, etc. This is all more or less plausible and can be a good *aide memoire*, but its historical truth is doubtful. ('M' was certainly a medieval invention – the Romans used ⊂|⊃ or ∞.)

A good starting-point for your class milestone can be:

HINCE • SUNT • ... • PASSUS • AD • DOMUM • SYLVIAE

('From here it is ... paces to Sylvia's house.')

The Latin genitive (Sylviae for Sylvia's etc.) should end in 'ae' for females and 'i' for males. Some present-day names work easily – Antonii, Roberti, etc. – others have to be tortured into shape: Wayni, Laurenae, etc.

To make milestone inscriptions metric, we suggest you estimate the number of metres to Sylvia's house and divide by 1.5 (because a *passus* is a double pace – about 1.5 metres). Thus 300 metres becomes CC PASSUS, 1500 metres is M PASSUS, and so on.

Note: the Romans always used upper-case letters for inscriptions. To include several names on the milestone, use:

HINCE • SUNT • ... • PASSUS • AD • DOMUM ... • ... • (name) PASSUS • AD • DOMUM ... • ... • PASSUS • AD • DOMUM • ...

and so on.

B3

Reading non-standard Roman numerals is an exercise to consolidate fluency. Children always look for the 'deliberate mistake'.

Look-up tables can be important, especially where data are irregular, as in timetables etc. Confidence in reading tables requires clarity about the meaning of row and column headings. The general method for reading tables should be:

1 Read and understand the table's title if it has one.
2 Read and understand the row and column headings.
3 Read the cell where the row and column intersect.

B4

Children are fascinated by big numbers. Some languages, e.g. Hindi, have special words where English has none (*lakh* = 100 000; *crore* = 10 million, etc.). Like all history, this book provides many starting-points for multicultural discussions. (As L P Hartley wrote: 'The past is a foreign country: they do things differently there.')

B5

This Activity Sheet explores links between literacy and numeracy; each gains from the other. Number-words and foreign words can enhance our understanding of our own language.

Children love to construct their own word-searches. Try word-searches in other areas too, e.g. shape and space, music, geography, etc.

Everyday Numbers

NAME .... DATE ....

You will need Resource Sheet R4 'Roman Numerals'.

Using Roman numerals, write in all twelve numbers on this clock.

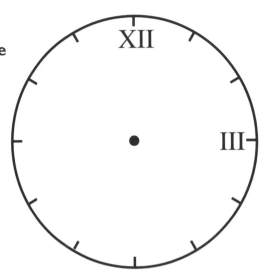

How old are you? .... **years** (in Roman)

How many months old are you? .... **months** (in Roman)

How old will you be in 20 years' time? .... **years** (in Roman)

How many pupils are in your class? .... **pupils** (in Roman)

Complete the following Roman sums in Roman numerals.

II + III = ...

VI + IV = ...

II × III = ...

VI × IV = ...

Now write some problems of your own like those above.

Gladiator CHALLENGE

Write a story involving numbers, using only Roman numerals.

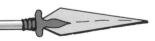

TRIVIUM Romans generally wrote numbers additively, not subtractively (VIIII and LXXXX, not IX and XC). Subtractive forms were used more in the Middle Ages.

A Roman Milestone

NAME .... DATE ....

See Resource Sheet R6 'Roman Inscriptions'

There are lots of numbers on this Roman milestone. The symbol ↓ is used for 50, instead of L, and D is written Ð.

Here is the same milestone with the numbers blanked out.

VIAM·FECEI·AB·REGIO· AD·CAPVAM·ET
IN·EA·VIA·PONTEIS·OMNEIS·MILIARIOS
TABELARIOSQVE·POSEIVEI·HINCE·SVN
NOVCERIAMMEILIA·LI ·CAPVAM·XXCI
MVRANVM·LXXIIII·COSENTIAM·CXXIII
VALENTIAM·CLXXX   AD·FRETVMAÐ
STATVAM·CCXXXI ·REGIVM·CCXXXVI
·SVMA·AF·CAPVAREGIVM·MEILIA·CCC
ET·EIDEM·PRAE TOR·IN   ·XXI
SICILIA·FVGITEIVOS·ITALICORVM
CONQ·VAEISIVEI·REDIDEIQVE
HOMINES·ÐCCCCXVII·   EIDEMQVE
PRIMVS·FECEI·VT·DE·AGRO·POPLICO
ARATORIBVS·CEDERENT·PAASTORES
FORVM·AEDISQVE·POPLICAS·HEIG·FECEI

Write in the Roman numbers.

VIAM • FECEI • AB • REGIO • AD • CAPUAM • ET
IN • EA • VIA • PONTEIS • OMNEIS • MILIARIOS
TABELARIOSQUE • POSEIVEI • HINCE • SUNT
NOVCERIAM • MEILIA • .... • CAPUAM • ....
MURANUM • .... • COSENTIAM • ....
VALENTIAM • .... • AD • FRETUM • AD
STATUAM • .... • REGIUM • ....
SUMA • AP • CAPUA • REGIUM • MEILIA • ....
ET • EIDEM • PRAETOR • IN
SICILIA • FUGITEIVOS • ITALICORUM
CONQUAEISIVEI • REDIDEIQUE
HOMINES • .... • EIDEMQUE
PRIMUS • FECEI • UT • DE • AGRO • POPLICO
ARATORIBUS • CEDERENT • PAASTORES
FORUM • AEDISQUE • POPLICAS • HEIC • FECEI

These numbers all appear on the milestone.
What does each one mean?

LI ....   XXCIIII ....   LXXIIII ....   CXXIII ....   CLXXX ....

CCXXXI ....   CCXXXVII ....   CCCXXI ....   DCCCCXVII ....

I built the road from Regium to Capua and on this road I erected all the bridges, milestones and postal stations. From here to Novceria it is 51 miles, to Capua 84, to Muranum 74, to Consentia 123, to Valentia 180, to the seashore where the statue is 231, to Regium 237. In all from Capua to Regium it is 321 miles. Moreover as Praetor in Sicily I tracked down Italic fugitive slaves and restored to their owners 917 persons. Moreover I was the first to establish that on public lands herdsmen must give way to farmers. At this place I built the forum and other public buildings.

Write your own class milestone, with distances in metres to different people's houses.

TRIVIUM The *Columna rostrata* includes over 20 (⊚) symbols, each representing 100 000 *aes* or bars of bronze, that is over 2 million *aes* in all. [In fact there were originally 32 such symbols on the inscription, representing 3 200 000 *aes*.]

Roman Multiplication

NAME .... DATE ....

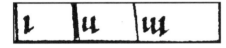

Multiplying using Roman numerals was fairly difficult, so look-up tables were useful. This table is from a thirteenth-century monastic manuscript.

🪙 **What do you notice about it?**

....

....

....

....

continue overleaf

The first three column headings are: I, II, III.

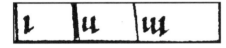

🪙 **What is the next column heading?**

....

What should it be?

....

📝 🪙 **What would be the next row on the table on the right?**

🪙 **Write out your own Roman multiplication table. Put one mistake in it. Then see if your friends can find the mistake.**

Can you find a multiplication mistake in the thirteenth-century table?

TRIVIUM In the Middle Ages, the final *i* in a number was often written *j* to prevent later alteration. Superscripts were also used. Thus, *iiij^M lb vij lb lb lxxxviij lb x s ij d* meant £4798, 10 shillings and 2 pence.

Big Numbers

NAME .... DATE ....

You will need Resource Sheet R5 'Big Numbers'.

Put these numbers in order, from lowest to highest:

L,   I,   V,   X,   C,   ⊂Ɔ.

....
lowest   highest

Now put these numbers in order:

ĪĪ,   ⌐X⌐,   (⊂Ɔ),   Þ,   ⌐ĪĪĪ⌐,   ((⊂Ɔ)) .

....
lowest   highest

This inscription from 260 BC celebrates a Roman naval victory over the Carthaginians:

(Auro)M • CAPTOM • NUMEI • .... •
(Argen)TOM • CAPTOM • PRAEDA • NUMEI • .... •
(Omne) • CAPTOM • AES • .... •

The gaps represent numbers. The literal translation is:

Gold • captured • coins • 3500 •
Silver • captured • booty • coins • 100 000
Total • loot • *aes* • 100 000
(repeated more than 20 times)

(The *aes* was the basic Roman money unit at this time.)

Fill in the gaps above with the appropriate Roman number symbols.

TRIVIUM The historian Pliny the Elder (AD 23–79) wrote: 'The ancient Romans had no number higher than a hundred thousand. Even today, when one multiplies this number one says "ten times a hundred thousand" and the like.'

Gladiator CHALLENGE

Write your own inscription with Roman numbers to celebrate winning an imaginary war and capturing lots of booty.

Roman Number Word–Search

NAME .... DATE ....

Many English words have Latin roots. The words below come from Roman number-words.

CENTURY	MILLENIUM	QUARTER	TRIPLET
DECEMBER	NOVEMBER	QUARTET	TRIPOD
DECIMAL	OCTAGON	SEPTEMBER	UNIFY
DECIMATE	OCTET	TRIANGLE	UNION
DUEL	OCTOBER	TRICE	UNISEX
DUET	OCTOPUS	TRICYCLE	UNISON
DUO	QUAD	TRIKE	UNITED
MILE	QUADRILATERAL	TRIMARAN	

How many can you find in this word-square? How many other words can you find?

(NB: The words can go horizontally, vertically or diagonally. List the row and then the column in which each word starts.)

	I	II	III	IV	V	VI	VII	VIII	IX	X	XI	XII	XIII	XIV	XV
I	Q	T	R	I	P	O	D	E	C	E	M	B	E	R	U
II	U	N	I	F	Y	I	U	N	I	S	E	X	W	N	R
III	A	Q	U	A	R	T	E	T	R	I	K	E	I	T	E
IV	R	U	U	L	O	C	T	O	P	U	S	T	T	G	T
V	T	A	D	A	A	L	A	M	I	C	E	D	R	R	S
VI	E	D	U	O	D	U	E	T	D	D	P	E	I	T	E
VII	R	R	E	W	S	P	C	P	R	W	T	C	P	U	H
VIII	M	I	L	L	E	N	I	U	M	I	E	I	L	E	C
IX	G	L	U	N	I	S	O	N	I	A	M	M	E	L	N
X	I	A	E	A	C	T	W	V	L	N	B	A	T	G	A
XI	O	T	R	I	C	Y	C	L	E	U	E	T	R	N	M
XII	C	E	N	T	U	R	Y	G	N	M	R	E	H	A	W
XIII	T	R	E	U	S	T	Y	I	L	E	B	I	C	I	N
XIV	E	A	T	I	A	X	O	C	T	O	B	E	R	R	B
XV	T	L	E	V	O	N	O	G	A	T	C	O	R	T	L

TRIVIUM The word 'millennium' was spelt 'millenium' in the seventeenth century. A 'millenarian' is someone who believes Christ will return and reign for a thousand years. Some words with 'mill' in them have nothing to do with thousands (milliners make hats; millers and millionaires wear them).

For each word you find, explain what it means and draw a picture to illustrate it.

Section C   Emperors, Gods, Coins and Calendars

Introduction

This section explores the Roman mind, which linked gods and planets in various mystical ways. If today we dismiss this as superstitious nonsense, we should ask whether our own minds are any more rational.

The Emperors were also sometimes linked with gods in terms of their supposed personal characteristics, giving a 'holy triangle'.

Extensions

C1

This calendar may not be authentic; however, it provides a convenient physical model to represent the passage of time. The pegs were probably moved as time passed.

At the top are the weekly day-Gods, presumably in order: Saturn, Sun, Moon, Mars, Mercury, Jupiter, Venus. On the left and right are the days I to XXX. It is unclear what happens on the 31st. In the centre are 24 peg-holes divided into pairs. The signs of the zodiac suggest that they represent the months. An alternative interpretation is that they relate to hours of the day (see Activity C3).

C2

Roman coinage changed over time. The Republican system presented here was in use about 100 years before the invasion of Britain. The names of the coins also represented fractions. It has a simple structure based on divisions of 12 and the *uncia* (a word meaning roughly 'unit' used in length (inch) and weight (ounce) as well as in coinage). The coin names tie in nicely with common Latin number words and prefixes (semi-, quadr, tri-, etc.).

When the Romans conquered Britain, a different coinage system was in use. The lowest denomination was a copper or bronze *quadrans*, the highest a gold *aureus* worth 3200 *quadrantes*.

The low-value copper or bronze coins were:

2 *quadrantes* = 1 *semis*   2 *asses* = 1 *dupondius*

2 *semisses* = 1 *as*   2 *dupondii* = 1 *sestertius*

These are the higher-value coins:

4 *sestertii* = 1 silver *quinarius*
2 *quinarii* = 1 silver *denarius*
$12\frac{1}{2}$ *denarii* = 1 gold *quinarius*
2 gold *quinarii* = 1 gold *aureus*

The price list is very conjectural. There is little evidence about Roman prices, apart from some graffiti found in Pompeii.

The Gladiator Challenge poem can be translated as follows:

$$\therefore\cdot\cdot\ -\ \cdot\ =\ \cdot\cdot\ \cdot\cdot$$
quincunx − uncia = triens

$$\therefore\cdot\cdot\ +\ \cdot\ =\ \text{S}^-$$
quincunx + uncia = semis

C3

Unlike the day, month and year, the week has no obvious astronomical meaning. What might our week have been if the planets Uranus and Pluto had been known in Roman times – would we have a nine-day week?

This activity can be extended to discuss other aspects of modular arithmetic (arithmetic of remainders). The mathematics of this activity rely on the fact that:

$24 \equiv 3 \pmod 7$

(Dividing 24 by 7 leaves a remainder of 3.) Thus, moving 24 places round the circle is equivalent to moving 3 places. Iterating this process, we visit all 7 vertices and return to the starting point.

C4

Roman dice, unlike ours, did not have equal probabilities. Even the cubic ones were irregularly weighted: they were made from hollow bone. Whether this was regarded as a defect is unknown, but it certainly complicates the mathematics.

The face probabilities for an *astragalus* must be determined empirically – throw it a lot of times, and count how often each face comes up. Of course, every *astragalus* is different.

The addition tables on the Activity Sheet lead to important results summarised by shading on the tables, namely:

+	O	E
O	E	O
E	O	E

C5

For more Activity Sheets on Hypatia, see *Mathematics from History: The Greeks* (pages 37–49), which also provides a fuller biography.

Slicing cones gives rise to the circle, ellipse, hyperbola and parabola, an important family of curves called the conics.

The notion of 'projecting' solids onto a plane (from 3-D to 2-D) is also important. A related question is: What shape shadows can you get...?

Gods and Calendars

NAME .... DATE ....

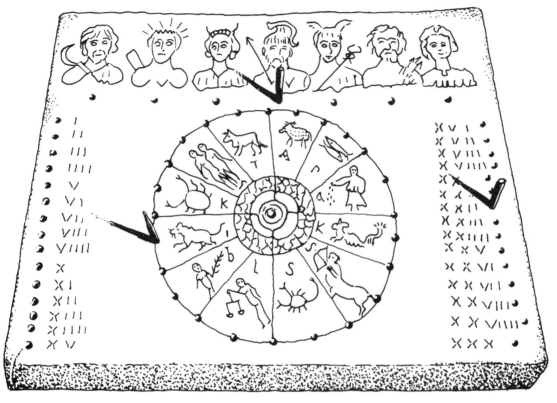

TRIVIUM Nobody knows where this calendar came from. It may even be a forgery.

🪙 **How do you think this Roman calendar worked?**

🪙 **Can you see any gods you recognise?**

🪙 **Complete the following to describe the calendar layout. The first line has been completed for you.**

• The 7 days of the week are along the top of the calendar.

• The 24 hours of the day are ....
....

• The 12 signs of the zodiac are ....
....

• There are also ....
....

 **CHALLENGE** **Design a calendar for your own use. (This could be a good group project to do with friends. You can include things you do at school, in different terms in the year, etc.)**

Fractions and Roman Coins

NAME .... DATE ....

You will need Resource Sheet R7 'Roman Coins'.

Using Resource Sheet R7, complete the following table. Some parts have been done for you.

coin	fraction of *as*	number of *unciae*	symbol	god
As	1	12	I	
Semis			S	Jupiter
Triens		4		
Quadrans				
Sextans			• •	
Uncia		1		

Here is a price list that might have been seen in Rome.

Work out the cost of each of the following:

2 loaves of bread: .... *unciae*

1 large and 1 small pot: .... *unciae*

> bread: 2 unciae per loaf
> hare: 1 semis
> large pot: 2 aes
> small pot: 1 aes
> groma: 10 aes
> beans: 1 triens per pound
> figs: 1 quadrans per pound
> olives: 1 sextans per pound

A Roman child has some *triens* and *quadrans* coins. How can she pay exactly for:

- something costing 7 *unciae*?
- something costing 8 *unciae*?
- something costing 9 *unciae*?

Are there any numbers of *unciae* that she can't pay exactly?

Every citizen and educated slave was expected to master the Roman monetary system. It took a lot of time at school, as the poet Horace commented in his *Ars Poetica*:

Gladiator CHALLENGE

Explain the calculations in this poem, and invent your own similar sums using Roman fractions.

> Roman children learn to divide the as
> By lengthy working into tiny parts.
> 'Son of Albanus, tell me: if we take
> An uncia from a quincunx, what is left?
> Be good enough to say 'A triens'. Fine!
> Your money will be guaranteed for life.
> We add an uncia: what does that make? 'Half.'

TRIVIUM The *quincunx* (⁙) was 5 *unciae*; a *denarius* was 10 *aes* (✕), a *quinarius* was 5 *aes* (Ⅴ), and a *scruple* was one-twenty-fourth of an *uncia*. (These definitions changed over time. In AD 14 there was a big devaluation, and a completely different system came into use.)

The Seven–Day Week

NAME .... DATE ....

The seven-day week is related to to the seven heavenly bodies (the Sun, the Moon and five visible planets) that were believed to circle the Earth.

The Moon, which moves fastest across the sky, was taken to be the nearest of these heavenly bodies. Saturn, which moves slowest across the sky, was believed to be the furthest away. The order was:

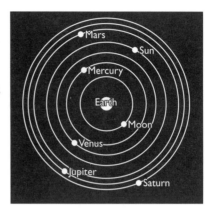

Moon	Mercury	Venus	Sun	Mars	Jupiter	Saturn
☽	☿	♀	☉	♂	♃	♄

🪙 **Which planets known today were unknown in Roman times?**

.... **and** ....

To the Romans each planet was also a god, and was associated with a day of the week as shown in this diagram.

🪙 **Imagine this diagram is a clock face. The hand takes an hour to move from I to II, and so on. It starts at I with Saturn.**

- Where is the hand after 24 hours?

- Where is it after 48 hours (2 days)?

- Where is it after 72 hours (3 days)?

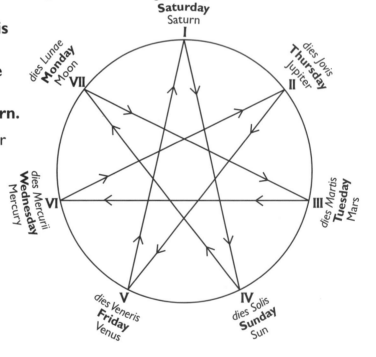

Continue to count round the heptagram for five days, then for one week.

TRIVIUM Every hour of every day was associated with a planet and a god. The first hour of Saturday was associated with Saturn, followed by Jupiter, Mars, the Sun, Venus, Mercury and the Moon. The eighth hour was associated with Saturn again, and so on. On the twenty-fifth hour — the first hour of Sunday — the Sun was the god; 24 hours later the Moon, and so on.

Games, Gods and Gambling

NAME .... DATE ....

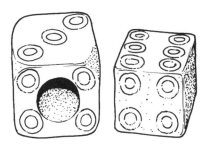

The Romans loved gambling. They also used dice for divination, or telling the future using the Gods.

Some Roman dice were rather like ours: six-faced and relatively symmetrical. Some were hollow, being cut from a long bone and ground down; others were filled in.

However, *tali* were much more varied. They were animal *astragali* (knuckle or heel bones). They were not symmetrical, and had only four faces they could land on. The scores were **1**, **3**, **4**, and **6**, as follows:

1: the flat and narrow side

3: the side opposite 4, broad and slightly concave

4: the upper side, broad and slightly convex

6: the side opposite 1, slightly hollow

As in many cultures, odd numbers were thought to be lucky.

🪙 **Circle the odd numbers above.**

🪙 **What do you reckon to be your lucky number?** ....

   Is it even or odd? ....

🪙 **If two *tali* are thrown and their numbers are added:**

   • What is the lowest total you can get? ....

   • What is the highest total you can get? ....

   • Are there totals between the lowest and highest which you cannot get? If so, which? ....

   • Do you think odd or even totals are more likely? ....

Draw a 4 x 4 table showing the totals you could get throwing two *tali*. Investigate what can happen when three *tali* are thrown.

TRIVIUM In some games, the Romans would throw four *tali*. The top score was obtained by throwing 1, 3, 4, 6 – one of each side. This was known as a 'Venus' throw. If a 1 was thrown, this was known as a 'dog' or 'vulture'.

Hypatia of Alexandria

NAME ....   DATE ....

Alexandria was an important centre of learning in three great ancient civilisations: Egypt, Greece and Rome.

About AD 400, representatives of the Christian church came to power in Rome. They were intolerant of 'heathens', and murdered many of them. The great Library and Museum of Alexandria were destroyed.

Among those who were murdered was Hypatia, probably the greatest mathematician of her time. She was said to be a fine teacher and very beautiful; but she rejected all lovers in favour of her study and her religion. She was taken from her chariot and killed by a mob.

Hypatia studied many branches of mathematics, including the theory of conic sections. These are the two-dimensional cross-sections of a cone.

🪙 **Which of the following shapes are possible when a cone is sliced?**

....

🪙 **What cross-sections result if you cut a cone as shown? Draw and describe these shapes.**

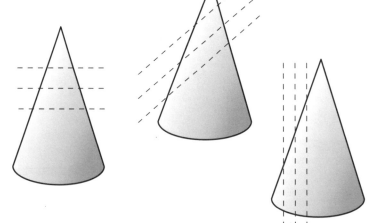

TRIVIUM Some people think the figure of St Catherine is based on Hypatia. Certainly they have a lot in common: both were virgins, beautiful and learned; and chariot wheels played a part in both their murders.

Gladiator CHALLENGE

Hypatia also studied how quickly the Earth moves round the Sun. How many degrees do you think that the Earth sweeps out round the Sun in one day? (A full year is 365.24 days, and there are 360 degrees in a full circle).

Section D   Measurement

Introduction

This section shows how Roman measures have influenced those in use today. Children do learn about imperial measure at home and in history, even if it has been banished from the mathematics classroom!

Many pre-metric measures were based on the human body. They also used various number-bases, often (but not always) multiples and divisors of 12. Using these measures can encourage mathematical sophistication.

The metric system was established by the French Revolutionaries, and it uses base 10 throughout. The metre was originally defined as one forty-millionth of the Earth's circumference.

Extensions

D1

Data on body measurements can provide a rich source for summaries (mean, median, interquartile range) and graphical techniques (such as the use of scatter diagrams). You can draw scatter diagrams of foot length against height, say, for boys and girls separately. Such activities allow you to investigate any differences between the sexes in level, variation or correlation.

D2

You can construct a steelyard in the classroom using a marked rod and weights. Then see whether you can verify in practice the theory that moments are equal:

(weight 1) × (distance 1) = (weight 2) × (distance 2)

D3

This activity provides an informal introduction to the geometry and trigonometry of similar triangles (triangles of the same shape, i.e. with the same angles but not necessarily the same side lengths).

A useful playground extension is to draw *big* triangles, including vertical ones (e.g. up a tree). This 'pavement mathematics' can be far more memorable and evocative than the itsy-bitsy paper-and-pencil variety!

D4

There is no substitute for making your own *groma*.

The *groma* had a central plumb line and four outer plumb lines. To make a straight line, you have to ensure that the central plumb line, an outer plumb line and a distant pole are in line.

The 'Egyptian triangle' with 3:4:5 sides can be used to illustrate the constancy of ratio in similar triangles (see Activity D3). It also illustrates Pythagoras' Theorem, because:

$$3^2 + 4^2 = 5^2$$

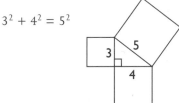

Triangles with sides 6:8:10, 30:40:50, and so on, are similar to this. Triangles with sides in the ratio 5:12:13 also satisfy the equation

$$a^2 + b^2 = c^2$$

the general solution to which is:

$$a = p^2 - q^2$$
$$b = 2pq$$
$$c = p^2 + q^2$$

The Romans undoubtedly knew this general rule, as did the Greeks and Babylonians.

D5

The shape of the corn measure is a frustum of a cone, and could have resulted from the 'slicing' explored in Activity C5. If drawn in plan, several on a table would look like this, with the smaller circles indicating the upper edge and the larger circles the lower edge.

The volume of a cone is $\frac{1}{3}\pi r^2 h$, i.e. one-third that of a cylinder with the same base and height. The volume of a frustum is the difference between the volumes of the two relevant cones.

The Measure of Man

NAME ....   DATE ....

The Romans used body parts as standard measures. The only problem was that they varied from person to person!

See how your measurements compare with the Roman standard.

	1 finger-width	1 palm-width	1 foot	1 (double) pace
Measure yours:	.... cm	.... cm	.... cm	.... cm
The Roman standard:	1 *digitus* = 1.85 cm	1 *palmus* = 7.4 cm = 4 *digiti*	1 *pes* = 29.5 cm = 4 *palmi*	1 *passus* = 148 cm = 5 *pedes*
Yours as % of the Roman standard:	.... %	.... %	.... %	.... %

For longer distances the Romans used:

1 *stadium* = 125 *passus*

1 *milliare* (or *mille passuum*) = 8 *stades* = 1000 *passus*

How many metres is:

1 *stadium*? .... m

1 *milliare*? .... m

For shorter distances the Romans used:

1 *uncia* = the width of a thumb = $\frac{1}{12}$ of 1 *pes*

How many centimetres are in 1 *uncia*? .... cm

**The Romans also used
1 *uncia* = width of thumb
and 1 cubit = from the elbow to the tip of the hand.
How many *unciae* do you think made a *pes*?
How many *unciae* made a cubit?**

TRIVIUM Leonardo da Vinci (1452–1519), the great artist and engineer, wrote of the Roman architect-engineer Vitruvius (first century BC): 'Vitruvius declares that Nature has thus arranged the measure of man: four fingers make one palm, and four palms make one foot; six palms make one cubit; four cubits make once a man's height; four cubits make a pace, and twenty-four palms make a man's height.'

Weighing Meat

NAME .... DATE ....

The Romans invented the *steelyard* around 200 BC. Butchers used it to weigh meat.

🪙 **Complete the following instructions:**

Instructions for Using a Steelyard

❋ Hold thy steelyard steady using the .... (or hang it).

❋ Put the meat ....

❋ Move .... until ....

❋ Read .... from the ....

Select from the following:
- on the hook
- the weight
- marked scale
- pivot-hook
- the arm is level
- the meat's weight

The scale on the steelyard was constructed using the following formula, which applies whenever the steelyard is in balance (horizontal).

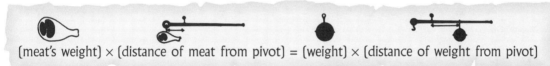

(meat's weight) × (distance of meat from pivot) = (weight) × (distance of weight from pivot)

For example, if the meat distance is 10cm and the weight distance is 20cm, then

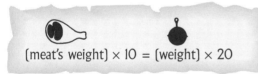

(meat's weight) × 10 = (weight) × 20

🪙 **If the weight weighs 1kg, what is the weight of the meat? .... kg**

🪙 **Fill in the gaps in the table.**

(kg)	(cm)	(kg)	(cm)
	20	1	10
	20	2	10
	20	2	20
	10	2	20
	15	3	15

Gladiator CHALLENGE

The Roman unit of weight, the *libra* or pound, was about 327g. One-twelfth of a *libra* was an *uncia*. How many grams were there in an *uncia*? Compare the *uncia* and *libra* with today's ounce and pound. (Today's ounce is 28.35g, and a pound is 16 ounces.)

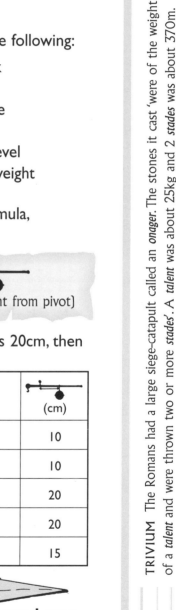

TRIVIUM The Romans had a large siege-catapult called an *onager*. The stones it cast 'were of the weight of a *talent* and were thrown two or more *stades*'. A *talent* was about 25kg and 2 *stades* was about 370m.

Walls and Ditches

NAME ....   DATE ....

People attacking a Roman fort could try to hide in the ditch outside. To prevent this, the sides of the ditch were put at an angle so the attackers could be seen from the top of the wall.

Using the angle of the slope, we can estimate the height of the wall, even after it has fallen down.

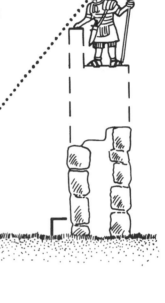

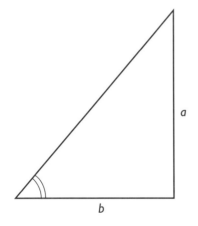

The method of calculation is first to measure the marked angle; then to draw a triangle with that angle. (See diagram.)

Measure the ratio *a/b*. This should be the same as the ratio of the height of the wall to the distance of the wall from the ditch. So the height of the wall is the distance of the wall from the ditch, multiplied by *a/b*.

If the distance to the wall is 10m, what is the height of the wall? ....m

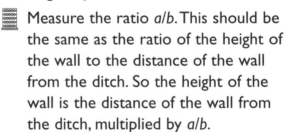

The ratio *a/b* is called the 'tangent' of the angle. Draw a graph to show how the tangent changes as the angle increases. Is the tangent of 45° midway between the tangents of 40° and 50°? Is the tangent of 50° midway between the tangents of 30° and 70°?

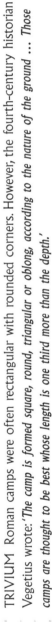

TRIVIUM Roman camps were often rectangular with rounded corners. However, the fourth-century historian Vegetius wrote: 'The camp is formed square, round, triangular or oblong, according to the nature of the ground ... Those camps are thought to be best whose length is one third more than the depth.'

The Groma

NAME .... DATE ....

In Roman surveying, two key elements are:

- straight lines
- right angles

The *groma* was crucial in obtaining both of these.

Imagine you are making a *groma*.

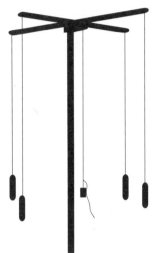

🪙 **Draw up a shopping list of all the things you would need.**

🪙 **Here is a price list. How much would your *groma* cost to make?**

wood: 50p per metre
string: 50p per metre
weights: £1 each
labour: £4 per hour

Here is one way to make a right angle.
You need some string a metre or
more in length.

- Fold your string into four equal parts (halve and halve again).
  Mark with a knot the place that is $\frac{1}{4}$ of the distance from one end.

- Fold the same string into three equal parts, and mark with another
  knot the place $\frac{1}{3}$ of the distance from the other end.

- Now bring the two ends together. If the sides are straight, the knots
  will be at two corners of a right-angled triangle.

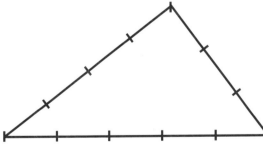

The Romans learnt this
method from the Egyptians.
All triangles with sides in the
ratio 3:4:5 are right-angled.

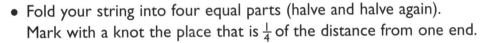

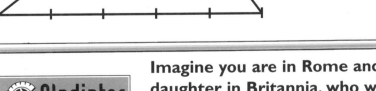

Gladiator CHALLENGE

Imagine you are in Rome and writing to your daughter in Britannia, who wants to know how to use the *groma*. Find out how it works and write a letter with diagrams explaining clearly how to use it.

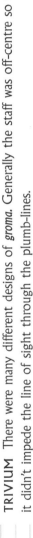

TRIVIUM There were many different designs of *groma*. Generally the staff was off-centre so that it didn't impede the line of sight through the plumb-lines.

Measuring Corn

NAME .... DATE ....

You will need Resource Sheet R6 'Roman Inscriptions'.

Describe the shape of the Roman corn measure at the bottom-left of Resource Sheet R6.

Draw a plan (a view from the top) showing several such corn measures on a table.

Corn and grain can be measured by capacity and volume (litres or pints) and by weight (kilograms or pounds).

The volume of this corn measure is about 50 pints.

Estimate the weight of corn that it holds. ....

Convert the above into litres and kilograms.
(1 pint = 568ml, 1 pound = 454g)

When full the corn weighs .... kg and is .... litres in volume.

What would be the weight of 1 litre of corn?
Is this heavier or lighter than 1 litre of water?
Would it float?

TRIVIUM Pure water weighs 1g per ml, or 1kg per litre. A cubic metre (100cm × 100cm × 100cm) is 1 million cm³ = 1 million ml, and 1 cubic metre of water weighs 1 million g = 1000kg = 1 tonne.
1 Roman pound (*libra*) = 327g, 28% less than a modern pound.

Section E Shape and Pattern in Roman Art

Introduction

This Section celebrates the immense richness of geometric design found in Roman mosaics and other artefacts. We may not know the details of mosaic-makers' training, but their work clearly required considerable mathematical sophistication. They must have understood not only symmetry and pattern in all guises, but also the aspects of computation and measurement required to create effective mosaics.

Extensions

E1

A useful challenge is to draw a square with one line through it so that the area of the square is divided equally.

Pupils could be restricted to straight lines, or lines through the centre, or lines not through the centre, or patterns with reflective or rotational symmetry. The shape being halved could also be a rectangle, circle, ellipse, etc.

One testing question is whether there is any shape that cannot be cut in half by a straight line.

E2

North Africa is a rich source for cross-curricular studies – geography, history, language, RE, and history of maths and science. Modern science owes a great deal to its African and Islamic heritage.

This elliptical amphitheatre can be used to discuss the words 'ellipse', 'oval', 'ovoid' and 'egg-shaped', which are often confused. The only one of these terms which is mathematically defined is 'ellipse'. It can be defined in various ways, but for our purposes an ellipse is a closed section of an infinite cone. Note that by this definition a circle is a special case of an ellipse, just as a square is a rectangle and a rectangle is a quadrilateral. (See Activity Sheets B3 and C5 for further study of conic sections.)

'Ovoid' means 'egg-shaped'; and both terms tend to be used for 2-dimensional (plane) figures, whereas eggs are undeniably 3-dimensional.

E3

This Activity aims to expand pupils' skills of visualisation and geometric intuition. It also develops their vocabulary and descriptive powers, making important links between numeracy and mathematics on the one hand and literacy and oracy on the other.

E4

There are many patterns linking numbers and triangles; Pascal's Triangle is perhaps the best known. (The top row of Pascal's Triangle is a single 1, and subsequent rows are generated by adding the pairs of numbers directly above.) If odd numbers are shaded in on Pascal's Triangle (A), a different pattern results, known as Sierpinski's Gasket (B).

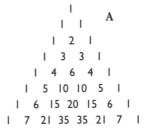
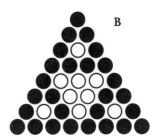

In the number pattern given on the sheet, the pattern of construction is simpler and leads to alternation between odd and even along each row.

E5

The *pelta* can be drawn using compasses, but freehand construction is more authentic!

The Gladiator Challenge is not straightforward. First you must express the required area in terms of its constituent parts:

= (large semicircle) − 2 × (small semicircle)

$$= \tfrac{1}{2} \times \pi \times (2a)^2 - 2 \times \tfrac{1}{2} \times \pi \times a^2$$

(where each square is of side $2a$)

$$= \pi a^2$$

As a percentage of the whole, this is

$$\approx 39.32\%$$

If the solid square is taken into account, the percentage of black increases to

$$4\pi a^2 + (2a)^2/36a^2 = (\pi + 1)/9 \approx 46\%.$$

Mosaics

NAME .... DATE ....

You will need Resource Sheet R9 'Mosaic Designs'.

🪙 **How many of the patterns A to R can you find on this Roman floor from Silchester?**

🪙 **On the table: tick**

(a) **if the pattern is in the Silchester floor mosaic;**

(b) **if it has reflective symmetry;**

(c) **if it has rotational symmetry.**

🪙 **Now, in columns (d) and (e), estimate how many white stones and how many black stones would be needed to complete each pattern, if 1000 stones are needed for the whole pattern.**

		(a)	(b)	(c)	(d) white	(e) black
A						
B						
C						
D						
E						
F						
G						
H						
I						
J						
K						
L						
M						
N						
O						
P						
Q						
R						

TRIVIUM Roman mosaics were make up of little squares of coloured stone, tile and glass. The Latin name for such a stone was *tessera*, from the Greek word for 'four' – a square having four sides and four angles.

Gladiator CHALLENGE

Draw your own mosaic design using patterns such as the above.

Rome in Africa

NAME ....   DATE ....

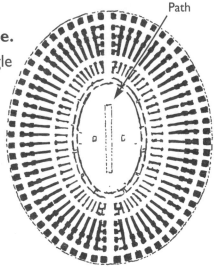

Many of the best Roman sites are in Africa: Timgad in Algeria, Leptis in Libya, and El Jem in Tunisia.

El Jem was one of the finest cities in the world during the second and third centuries AD when it was known as Thysdrus. El Jem has some magnificent mosaics, and its amphitheatre, shown here, is the best-preserved in the world.

Path

0 10 20 30 40 50m

Which of the following best describes the shape of this amphitheatre? Tick one.
- circle   • square   • ellipse   • rectangle

How many paths are there into the amphitheatre?

Look at the plan of the amphitheatre. Estimate:
- the length and width of the plan: .... cm
- the length and width of the amphitheatre: .... m

Now measure the lengths:
- The length and width of the plan are .... and .... cm.
- The length and width of the amphitheatre are .... and .... m.

Calculate the ratio of the length to the width of the amphitheatre: ....

Compare this ratio with the length-to-width ratio of other ellipses that you find.

The Colosseum in Rome is similar to the El Jem amphitheatre, but it is 188m long and 156m wide. How much bigger is this than the El Jem amphitheatre, as a percentage? If the Colosseum can seat 45,000 spectators, how many do you think could sit in the El Jem amphitheatre?

TRIVIUM The El Jem amphitheatre has three floors of galleries with 64 arches on each.

Shape, Space and Cross-Sections

NAME .... DATE ....

On the left is the corn measure you may already have examined in Activity D5. In this Activity, we will look at its shape.

On the right is a cone.

🪙 **Draw over the cone so that you get the same shape as the corn measure.**

🪙 **What other shapes can you get from other parts of the cone? Draw and describe them.**

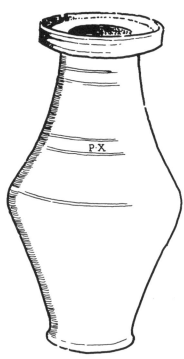

Here is another Roman measure. It is marked 'P·X', which means that it could hold water weighing ten Roman pounds.

🪙 **What shapes could you get from this Roman measure by cutting it in various ways? Draw and describe them.**

Congius Farnesianus
(Naples, AD 75. 24cm high.)

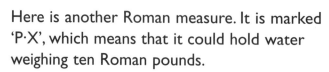

Draw as many shapes as you can that could give a circular cross-section when you cut them.

© Channel Four Learning Ltd 1999

Mosaic from Pompeii

NAME .... DATE ....

To draw this mosaic you need a grid of 14 x 14 squares.

Complete the lines in the lower half of the mosaic grid on the Resource Sheet. Shade it in.

How many triangles can you find in this large triangle? ....

Shade in the odd numbers in these triangles.

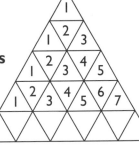

Try to work out the numbers for the bottom rows of the '1' and '3' triangles.

Gladiator CHALLENGE

Can you work out the numbers for the whole of the '5' triangle?
What do you notice about these patterns?

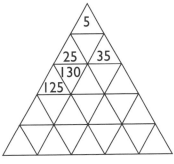

TRIVIUM Roman surveyors used triangles when they made roads. By measuring the distances and angles of three places from each other, they could work out exactly where they were.

The Pelta Mosaic Pattern

NAME .... DATE ....

This mosaic uses the square and the *pelta*, which is drawn like this using three semicircles:

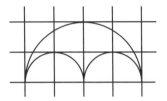

Mosaic from Hadrian's Villa at Tivoli

You can draw the curves either freehand or using compasses.

● **Complete this drawing; then make up some of your own.**

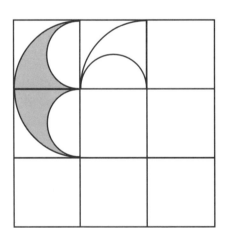

TRIVIUM The *pelta* is sometimes said to have been the shape of the shield used by the Amazons. It is also called the 'axe-shape'.

Gladiator CHALLENGE

What percentage of this *pelta* design is made of black stones, and what percentage of white? Check your estimate with others.

Roman Britain

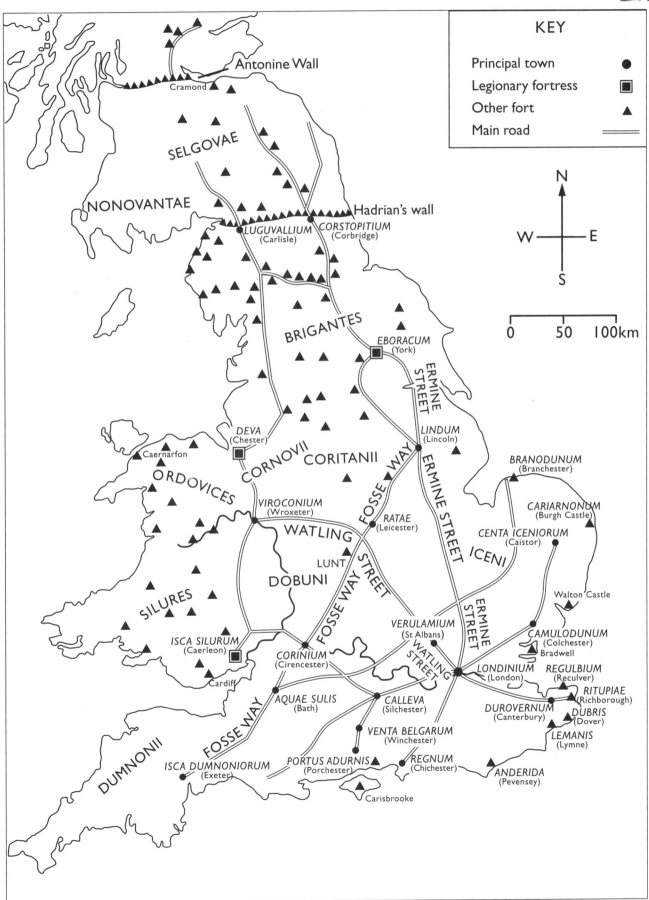

KEY

- Principal town ●
- Legionary fortress ▣
- Other fort ▲
- Main road ═══

N W E S

0   50   100km

Antonine Wall
Cramond

SELGOVAE

NONOVANTAE

Hadrian's wall

LUGUVALLIUM
(Carlisle)

CORSTOPITIUM
(Corbridge)

BRIGANTES

EBORACUM
(York)

ERMINE STREET

DEVA
(Chester)

CORNOVII

CORITANII

Caernarfon

ORDOVICES

VIROCONIUM
(Wroxeter)

LINDUM
(Lincoln)

BRANODUNUM
(Branchester)

CARIARNONUM
(Burgh Castle)

CENTA ICENIORUM
(Caistor)

ICENI

FOSSE WAY

RATAE
(Leicester)

WATLING

LUNT

DOBUNI

STREET

FOSSE WAY

SILURES

ISCA SILURUM
(Caerleon)

Cardiff

CORINIUM
(Cirencester)

FOSSE WAY

AQUAE SULIS
(Bath)

CALLEVA
(Silchester)

VERULAMIUM
(St Albans)

ERMINE STREET

WATLING STREET

CAMULODUNUM
(Colchester)
Bradwell

Walton Castle

LONDINIUM
(London)

REGULBIUM
(Reculver)

RITUPIAE
(Richborough)

DUROVERNUM
(Canterbury)

DUBRIS
(Dover)

LEMANIS
(Lymne)

VENTA BELGARUM
(Winchester)

REGNUM
(Chichester)

ANDERIDA
(Pevensey)

DUMNONII

ISCA DUMNONIORUM
(Exeter)

PORTUS ADURNIS
(Porchester)

Carisbrooke

Timeline of the Roman Occupation of Britain

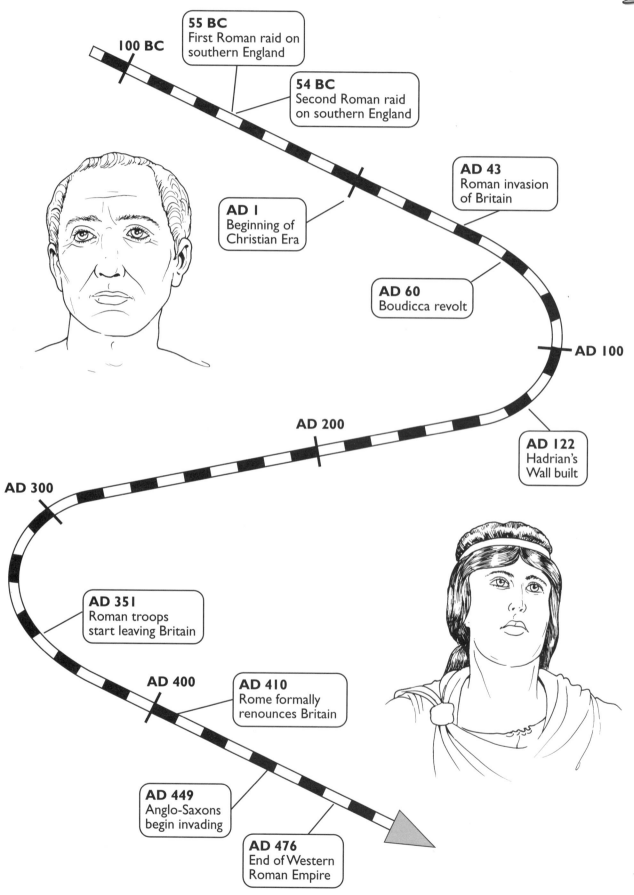

100 BC

55 BC
First Roman raid on southern England

54 BC
Second Roman raid on southern England

AD 43
Roman invasion of Britain

AD 1
Beginning of Christian Era

AD 60
Boudicca revolt

AD 100

AD 122
Hadrian's Wall built

AD 200

AD 300

AD 351
Roman troops start leaving Britain

AD 400

AD 410
Rome formally renounces Britain

AD 449
Anglo-Saxons begin invading

AD 476
End of Western Roman Empire

The Roman Empire

Extent of the Roman Empire

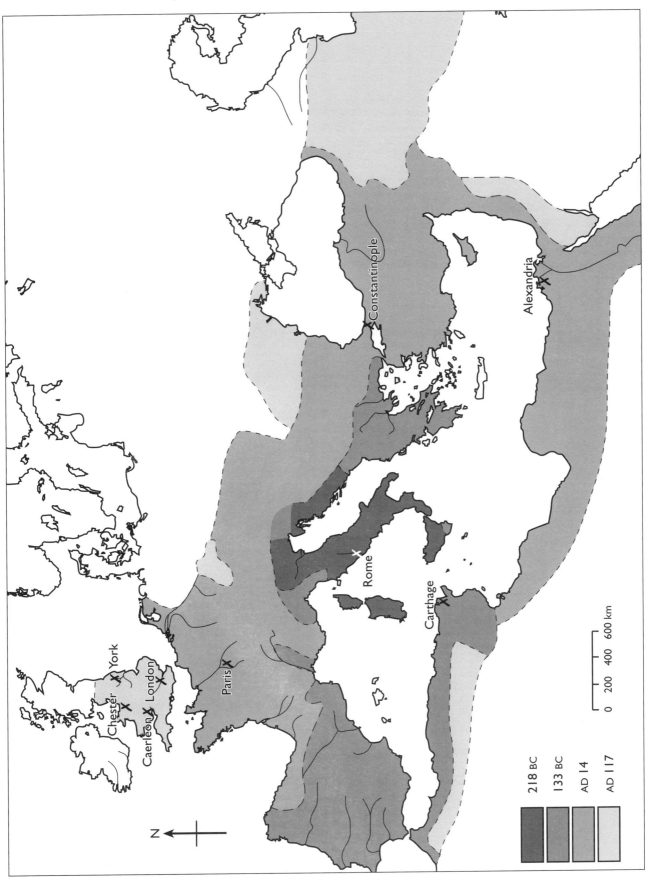

Roman Numerals

The seven main Roman number symbols were (and still are) combined in many different ways. They can form every number from 1 to 4999.

I	V	X	L	C	D	M or (I)
unus	*quinque*	*decem*	*quinqua-ginta*	*centum*	*quingenti*	*mille*
1	5	10	50	100	500	1000

A table of Roman numerals from a German book, 1524

An unusual 24-hour clock at Greenwich Observatory – what time does it say?

A multiplication table from a thirteenth-century manuscript – can you find the error in it?

A receipt dated 1410 that uses Roman numerals

Big Numbers

For larger numbers, the Romans had several symbols. They often used φ or ∞ instead of M to mean 1000. (Some people think that the Roman 'D' for 500 came from ▷, or half the φ sign.)

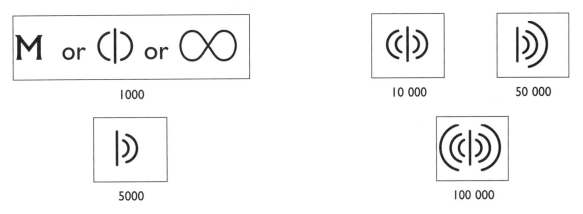

M or (|) or ∞
1000

((|))
10 000

|))
50 000

|)
5000

((|))
100 000

A b̄ar above could mean 'multiply by 1000': so V̄IXXXIX means 6039.

The b̄ar was also used to distinguish numbers from letters, e.g. ĪĪĪ VIR means 3 *vir* (3 men).

A 'frame' ⌐⌐ meant 'multiply by 100 000'. So ⌐I⌐ was 100 000, and ⌐X⌐ was one million.

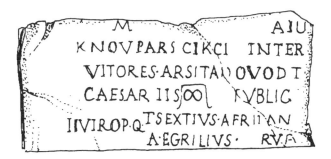

'Caesar sesterces 100 millions'.
'The symbol ∞ means 1000 × 100 000 or 100 million.

Roman Inscriptions

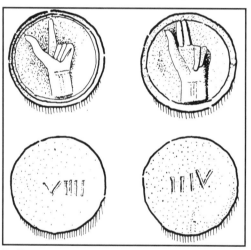

A Roman milestone on the Via Popilia

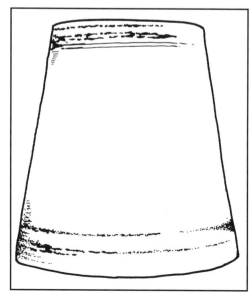

B Roman game counters showing finger signs and numerals

D Inscription on the *Columna rostrata*

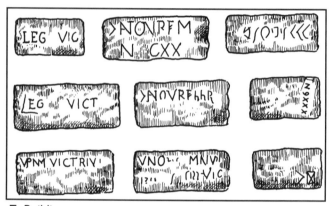

E Building stone

F Tablet

C Corn measure

G Stone coffin

Roman Coins

£

p

Today we have just two words for coins: 'pound' and 'penny'.

The Romans had many words for coins. They had six main coins.

name	symbol	description
as	I	The *as*, or pound, was the basic unit (plural *asses, aes* or *aurei*). It generally had the symbol I on it, with the two-faced head of the god Janus on one side and a boat prow on the other.
semis	S	Half an *as* was a *semis*. Its symbol was S, and its god was Jupiter.
quadrans	⁝	A quarter of an *as* or half a *semis* was a *quadrans*. Its symbol was three pellets, and its god was Hercules.
uncia	•	One-twelfth of an *as* was an *uncia* (ounce). Its symbol was a single dot • or pellet. The *uncia* usually showed the god Roma or Bellona.
triens	∷	One-third of an *as* (or 4 *unciae*) was a *triens*. Its symbol was four pellets. Minerva was the usual god on a *triens* coin.
sextans	••	The *sextans* was one-sixth of an *as*, or 2 *unciae*. Its god was generally Mercury, and its symbol was two pellets.

How many of these coins can you name?

Mosaic Grid

Mosaic from Pompeii

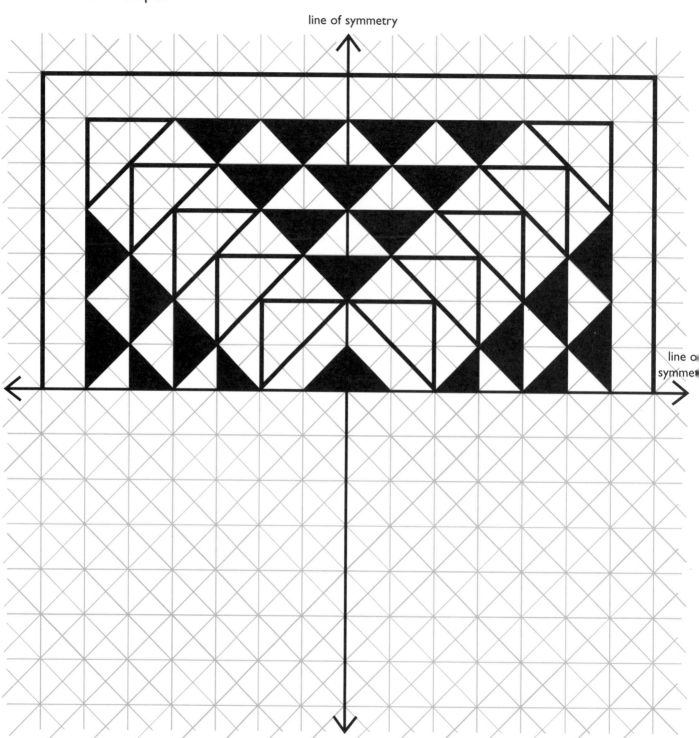

line of symmetry

line of symmetry

What other lines of symmetry are there in the completed pattern?

Mosaic Designs

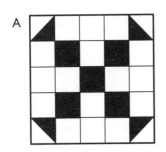

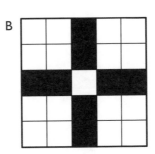

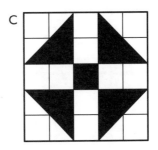

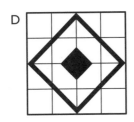

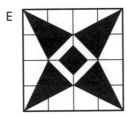

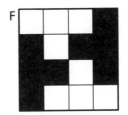

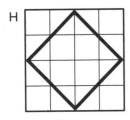

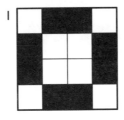

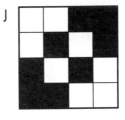

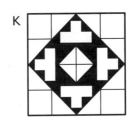

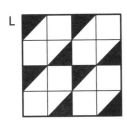

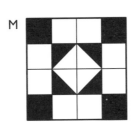

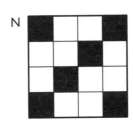

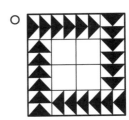

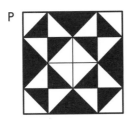

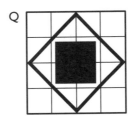

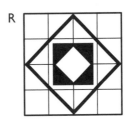

The above designs can be seen in Roman mosaic patterns, such as the one at Silchester (see Activity E1).

Duodecim Scripta ('Twelve Lines')

XXV	I	XXIV
XXVI	II	XXIII
XXVII	III	XXII
XXVIII	IV	XXI
XXIX	V	XX
XXX	VI	XIX
XXXI	VII	XVIII
XXXII	VIII	XVII
XXXIII	IX	XVI
XXXIV	X	XV
XXXV	XI	XIV
XXXVI	XII	XIII

Rules of *Duodecim Scripta*

- Players start with six pieces (black or white) on square I.
- The aim of the game is to get your pieces round the board to **XXXVI**.
- Black starts; players move alternately.
- To decide your move, throw three dice. Then move up to three of your pieces forward, so that the *total* number of squares moved equals the *total* on the three dice.
- If you land on a square with an opponent's piece on it, then the opponent's piece returns to I.
- If two or more opponent's pieces are on a square, then you cannot occupy that square.
- The winner is the first player to get all their pieces to the end.

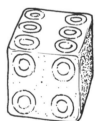

Record of Achievement

Name ....

Date ....

Before I began these activities I thought that ....

....

....

My favourite activity was ....

I liked it because ....

....

....

The activity I found most difficult was ....

....

because ....

....

....

I have learnt that ....

....

....

I would like to have more practice with ....

....

....

Mathematics from History: The Romans was written by John Bibby.

Edited by Liz Meenan, Alec Edgington and James Griffin
Designed by Oxford Designers and Illustrators
Printed by KSC

John Bibby is Honorary Visiting Fellow in Mathematics at the
University of York. He has written widely in the fields of statistics
and mathematical education, and has been actively involved with
several projects teaching multicultural mathematics and mathematics
through history. He is the founder and owner of QED, a resource
centre based in York specialising in mathematics.

The photographs on Activity Sheets E1 and E4 are reproduced by
kind permission of Tarquin Publications.